365 Days

Into Intimacy _with_ God

Dearest Debbie,

Blessings As you Step Daily Into the Intimacy with God. May It Change your Soul~ Love you~

Diane Andrews

DIANE ANDREWS

LCCN: SEL045000   Self-help/journaling
SEL016000   Self-help/personal growth/happiness
REL006110   Religion/biblical meditations/general

Books in Quantities of 1 to 18 per box
may be purchased through
Capture Books
5856 S. Lowell Blvd. Ste 32-202
Littleton, Colorado 80123
www.CaptureBookstore.com
e-mail: lb.CaptureBooks@aol.com
303-794-1957

Full Cover Design and Interior Photos: Kathryn K. Swezy
Interior Design: Tracy Fagan, FireballCreative.net
Eunice Bollinger wrote some difficult devotions
in the Old Testament.
Editors: Laura Bartnick, Marilyn Bay Drake,
Charmayne Hafen and Carole Stutzman,
Proofreader: Sue Lockwood Summers
Special thanks to my husband Rev. Michael Andrews
Thanks goes to the editors of the Phillips Translation,
the NIV, the NASB, the New Living Translation, the Holman
Christian Bible and the New King James Bible for the verses
contained herein.
ISBN: 978-0-9971625-8-5 (paperback)
ISBN: 978-0-9971625-7-8 (case laminate)

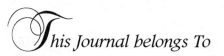

This Journal belongs To

_____

From

_____

Winter

20_____

In the beginning God created
the heavens and the earth.

Genesis 1:1 ~ NIV

Describe the most beautiful place you have ever seen. Name one reason God put creativity first. How does this truth bring confidence to your own creativity?

20____

ome to me, all you who are weary and burdened,
and I will give you rest.

Matthew 11:28 ~ NIV

Describe a moment you found rest with Jesus.

20_____

ear not, I have redeemed you;
I have called you by name; you are mine.

Isaiah 43:1 ~ NKJV

How does this verse call you into fellowship and companionship with God?

*Peace I leave with you; my peace I give to you.
Not as the world gives do I give to you.
Let not your hearts be troubled,
neither let them be afraid.*

John 14:27 ~ ESV

How does peace change your times of trouble?

_____

_____

_____

_____

_____

_____

_____

_____

_____

_____

_____

_____

_____

_____

_____

_____

_____

20_____

*You, God, are awesome in your sanctuary;
the God of Israel gives power and strength
to His people. Praise be to God!*

Psalm 68:35 ~ NIV

In what ways has God been your sanctuary and refuge?

_____

_____

_____

_____

_____

_____

_____

_____

_____

_____

_____

_____

_____

_____

_____

_____

_____

_____

_____

_____

20_____

*But grow in the grace and knowledge of
our Savior Jesus Christ. To him be the glory
both now and forever! Amen.*

2 Peter 3:18 ~ NIV

Write praises to God for His glory, grace, and knowledge.

7  **anuary**

20_____

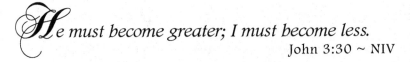
e must become greater; I must become less.

John 3:30 ~ NIV

Are you ready to stop being greater so you can enjoy the
freedom of forgetting about yourself?

20_____

Weeping may last through the night,
but joy comes with the morning.

Psalm 30:5 ~ NLT

Write about a moment in your life when weeping turned into
Joy! "Rejoice, again I say, Rejoice!"

_____
_____
_____
_____
_____
_____
_____
_____
_____
_____
_____
_____
_____
_____
_____
_____
_____
_____

20____

"*It is more blessed to give than to receive.*"

Acts 20:35 - ESV

Have you learned yet how to receive from others? And how is God calling you to give to others?

20_____

hey are like trees planted along the riverbank,
bearing fruit each season. Their leaves never wither,
and they prosper in all they do.

Psalm 1:3 ~ NLT

How is your spiritual life? Are you bearing fruit? Are you
prospering in all you do?

_____

_____

_____

_____

_____

_____

_____

_____

_____

_____

_____

_____

_____

_____

_____

_____

_____

_____

20_____

*or we are God's masterpiece. He has created us
anew in Christ Jesus, so we can do
the good things He planned for us long ago.*
Ephesians 2:10 ~ NLT

You are a masterpiece! Describe what it looks like.

_____
_____
_____
_____
_____
_____
_____
_____
_____
_____
_____
_____
_____
_____
_____
_____

anuary

20_____

My life is an example to many, because You have been my strength and protection.

Psalm 71:7 ~ NLT

How is your life an example of God's Love?

20_____

*Let us run with endurance the race
that God has set before us.*

Hebrews 12:1 ~ NLT

What race is God calling you to be faithful in?

_____
_____
_____
_____
_____
_____
_____
_____
_____
_____
_____
_____
_____
_____
_____
_____
_____
_____

*For I am the Lord your God who takes hold of
your right hand and says to you,
Do not fear; I will help you.*
Isaiah 41:13 ~ NIV

How have you overcome fear through God's help?

_____

_____

_____

_____

_____

_____

_____

_____

_____

_____

_____

_____

_____

_____

_____

_____

_____

20_____

Great is His faithfulness;
His mercies begin afresh each morning.

Lamentations 3:23 ~ NLT

Through God's faithfulness, how have you experienced His
mercies?

_____

_____

_____

_____

_____

_____

_____

_____

_____

_____

_____

_____

_____

_____

_____

_____

_____

_____

20_____

"While I, Daniel, was trying to make sense of what I was seeing, suddenly there was a humanlike figure standing before me."

Daniel 8:15 ~ MSG

Life can be so confusing. Where do you turn? Who do you ask for help?

_____

_____

_____

_____

_____

_____

_____

_____

_____

_____

_____

_____

_____

_____

_____

_____

_____

_____

20_____

God is our refuge and strength,
a very present help in trouble.

Psalm 46:1 ~ KJV

When was the last time of trouble that God was your refuge
and strength?

20_____

hey recognized him as the same man who used to sit begging at the temple gate called Beautiful, and they were filled with wonder and amazement at what had happened to him.

Acts 3:10 ~ NIV

In what areas of your life is God wanting you to be amazed and filled with wonder?

_____

_____

_____

_____

_____

_____

_____

_____

_____

_____

_____

_____

_____

_____

_____

_____

_____

20_____

or we walk by faith, not by sight.
2 Corinthians 5:7 ~ ESV

Who has modeled this kind of faith? Do you trust Him for everything?

20_____

But to you I cry, O Lord; and in the morning shall my prayer come to meet you.

Psalm 88:13 ~ AMP

When is your best time to get alone with God?

_____

_____

_____

_____

_____

_____

_____

_____

_____

_____

_____

_____

_____

_____

_____

20_____

White He was in Bethany, reclining at the table in the home of Simon the Leper, a woman came with an alabaster jar of very expensive perfume, made of pure nard. She broke the jar and poured the perfume on his head.

Mark 14:3 ~ NIV

What is the most costly gift that God has asked you to give?

_____

_____

_____

_____

_____

_____

_____

_____

_____

_____

_____

_____

_____

_____

20_____

As Jesus and his disciples were on their way,
he came to a village where a woman named Martha
opened her home to him.

Luke 10:38 ~ NIV

How does your hospitality bring others to your home?

20_____

The Lord is my Shepherd, I lack nothing.
Psalm 23:1 ~ NIV

How has the Lord been your Shepherd?

"*Forget the former things; do not dwell on the past. See, I am doing a good thing!*" *says The Lord.*
Isaiah 43:18~19 ~ NIV

What good thing has God done for you?

_____

_____

_____

_____

_____

_____

_____

_____

_____

_____

_____

_____

_____

_____

_____

_____

_____

20_____

I am content and at peace. As a child lies quietly in its mother's arms, so my heart is quiet within me.
Psalm 131:2 ~ GNT

How has the Holy Spirit quieted your soul?

_____

_____

_____

_____

_____

_____

_____

_____

_____

_____

_____

_____

_____

_____

_____

_____

_____

_____

*D*o you not know that your body is a temple of the Holy Spirit, who is in you, whom you have received from God? You are not your own; you were bought with a price. Therefore honor God with your body.

1 Corinthians 6:19-20 ~ NIV

How do you honor God with your body?

20_____

He said to her, "Daughter, your faith has healed you. Go in peace and be freed from your suffering."
Mark 5:34 ~ NIV

How does this verse challenge you to have a deeper faith?

January 28

20_____

Whenever you possibly can, do good to those who need it. Never tell your neighbor to wait until tomorrow if you can help them now.

Proverbs 3:27-28 ~ GNT

Journal about the last time you helped a neighbor or a friend. How did this make you feel?

_____

_____

_____

_____

_____

_____

_____

_____

_____

_____

_____

_____

_____

_____

_____

_____

_____

_____

_____

_____

20_____

My friend, fill your mind with those things that are good and that deserve praise: things that are true, noble, right, pure, lovely, and honorable.

Philippians 4:8 ~ GNT

Take time to list what is true, right, pure, lovely, and honorable in your life.

O Lord you have searched me and known me.
You know when I sit down and when I rise up;
you discern my thoughts from far away.

Psalm 139: 1~2 ~ NRSV

How do you feel knowing that God knows you?
He really knows you!

20____

*Be imitators of God, therefore, as dearly loved
children and live a life of love,
just as Christ loved us and gave himself up for us
as a fragrant offering and sacrifice to God.*

Ephesians 5:1-2 ~ NIV

What does it mean to be a imitator of God? What would that
look like in your soul and life?

20_____

esus said, "Put God's kingdom first.
Do what He wants you to do."
Matthew 6:33 ~ NIRV

What is God asking you to do?

_____

_____

_____

_____

_____

_____

_____

_____

_____

_____

_____

_____

_____

_____

_____

20_____

Keep your lives free from the love of money and be content with what you have, because God has said, "Never will I leave you; Never will I forsake you."
Hebrews 13:5 ~ NIV

What qualities of your life are you most contented with? What relationship offers more value to you than a thing you desire? What characteristics of God make you content?

20_____

rust in the Lord and do good; dwell in the land and enjoy safe pasture.

Psalm 37:3 ~ NIV

Right now, how are you specifically trusting God for your well-being and livelihood?

_____

_____

_____

_____

_____

_____

_____

_____

_____

_____

_____

_____

_____

_____

_____

_____

_____

_____

20_____

*C*alling His disciples to Him, Jesus said,
"Truly I tell you, this poor widow has put more
into the treasury than all the others. They all gave
out of their wealth; but she, out of her poverty,
put in everything-all she had to live on."

Mark 12:43-44 ~NIV

How is God calling you to give recklessly?

*O*ne of those listening was a woman from the city of
Thyatira named Lydia, a dealer in purple cloth.
She was a worshiper of God. The Lord opened her
heart to respond to Paul's message.

Acts 16:14 ~ NIV

Has the Lord ever opened your heart? How did you respond?

20_____

*I have always walked in your way and
have never strayed from it.*

Psalm 17:5 ~ GNT

What boundaries in your Christian life keep you from straying?

She had a sister, Mary, who sat before the Master, hanging on every word He said.

Luke 10:39 ~ MSG

Describe an intimate moment when you sat before your Master. Did you hear His voice?

_____

_____

_____

_____

_____

_____

_____

_____

_____

_____

_____

_____

_____

_____

_____

_____

_____

20_____

*ord, I am always with You; You hold me by my
right hand. You guide me with Your counsel.*

Psalm 73:23-24 ~ NIV

How does it feel to know that The Lord holds you by your right
hand, and guides you with His counsel?

_____

_____

_____

_____

_____

_____

_____

_____

_____

_____

_____

_____

_____

_____

_____

_____

_____

_____

20_____

*L*et all things be done
properly and in an orderly manner.

1 Corinthians 14:40 ~ NASB

What areas of your life is God wanting done properly and in
am orderly manner? Ask God to help you!

20_____

*rise, cry out to in the night,
as the watches of the night begin; pour out your heart
like water in the presence of The Lord.*

Lamentations 2:19 ~ NIV

Journal about the last moment you poured out your heart before God!

_____
_____
_____
_____
_____
_____
_____
_____
_____
_____
_____
_____
_____
_____
_____
_____
_____
_____

20_____

*od blessed the seventh day and made it holy,
because on it He rested from all the work of creating
that He had done.*

Genesis 2:3 ~ NIV

How do you rest on the seventh day?

_____

_____

_____

_____

_____

_____

_____

_____

_____

_____

_____

_____

_____

_____

_____

_____

_____

20_____

am worn out, O Lord; have pity on me! Give me strength; I am completely exhausted.

Psalm 6:2 ~ GNT

Describe a time when the Lord gave you strength in your exhaustion.

_____

_____

_____

_____

_____

_____

_____

_____

_____

_____

_____

_____

_____

_____

_____

_____

_____

20_____

Your beauty should not come from outward adornment, such as braided hair and the wearing of gold jewelry and fine clothes. Instead, it should be that of your inner self, the unfading beauty of a gentle and quite spirit, which is of great worth in God's sight.

1 Peter 3:3-4 ~ NIV

How is your soul?

20_____

*he Lord does not look at the things man looks at.
Man looks at the outward appearance,
but The Lord looks at the heart.*

1 Samuel 16:7 ~ NIV

How is your heart?

_____

_____

_____

_____

_____

_____

_____

_____

_____

_____

_____

_____

_____

_____

_____

_____

_____

_____

20_____

Carry each others' burdens,
and in this way you will fulfill the law of Christ.
Galatians 6:2 ~ NIV

Are you carrying another's burdens? Has someone done that for you?

_____

_____

_____

_____

_____

_____

_____

_____

_____

_____

_____

_____

_____

_____

_____

_____

_____

_____

16 February

20_____

There is a time for everything...
a time to search and a time to give up,
a time to keep and a time to throw away.

Ecclesiastes 3:1, 6 ~ NIV

What time are you in?

_____

_____

_____

_____

_____

_____

_____

_____

_____

_____

_____

_____

_____

_____

_____

_____

20_____

et us give thanks to God!
He wins the battle for us
because of what our Lord Jesus Christ has done.

1 Corinthians 15:57 ~ NIRV

What battle has He won for your life? Give thanks to God!

20_____

each us to count our days.

Psalm 90:12 ~ NRSV

How do you make the best use of your days?

20____

*oses said to the people, "Do not be afraid,
stand firm, and see the deliverance that The Lord will
accomplish for you today; for the Egyptians whom you
see today you will never see again, The Lord will fight
for you; and you have only to keep still."*

Exodus 14:13-14 ~ NRSV

What situation are you standing firm in? Do you believe God
will fight for you in your situation?

_____

_____

_____

_____

_____

_____

_____

_____

_____

_____

_____

_____

_____

_____

_____

_____

_____

20_____

*O*pen *my eyes so that I can see*
the wonderful truths in your law.

Psalm 119:18 ~ NIRV

Spend some time writing a prayer that God would open your
eyes to the wonderful truths in heaven.

20____

ince you are eager to have spiritual gifts, try to excel in gifts that build up the church.

1 Corinthians 14:12 ~ NIV

In what ways have your spiritual gifts impacted your church?

_____

_____

_____

_____

_____

_____

_____

_____

_____

_____

_____

_____

_____

_____

_____

_____

_____

22 February

20_____

God is our refuge and strength,
a very present help in trouble.

Psalm 46:1 ~ NRSV

How has God been a refuge to you? How has that given you
strength?

_____

_____

_____

_____

_____

_____

_____

_____

_____

_____

_____

_____

_____

_____

_____

20_____

*D*raw near to God and He will draw near to you.

James 4:8 ~ NSAB

Describe a moment when you drew near to God. Where were you? How did it change you?

24 February

20_____

I wait patiently for The Lord ;
He turned to me and heard my cry.

Psalm 40:1 ~ NIV

What request from God are you patiently waiting for?

_____

_____

_____

_____

_____

_____

_____

_____

_____

_____

_____

_____

_____

_____

_____

_____

_____

20_____

*he Spirit's presence is shown in some way
in each person for the good of all.*
1 Corinthians 12:7 ~ GNT

How has the Spirit of God shown Himself in your life?

20_____

*Be generous, and you will be prosperous.
Help others, and you will be helped.*

Proverbs 11:25 ~ GNT

How has God called you to be generous? How has your
generosity helped others in your life?

_____

_____

_____

_____

_____

_____

_____

_____

_____

_____

_____

_____

_____

_____

_____

_____

 ebruary 27

20____

We must remember the words of
The Lord Jesus Christ.
He said, "it is more blessed to give than to receive."
Acts 20:35 ~ NIRV

Describe a time that you gave generously and how it
blessed you.

_____

_____

_____

_____

_____

_____

_____

_____

_____

_____

_____

_____

_____

_____

_____

_____

_____

20_____

*Let us love, not in a word or speech,
but in truth and action.*

1 John 3:18 ~ NRSV

How has the Lord loved you? How have you loved Him back in truth and action?

20_____

he only thing that really counts
is faith that shows itself through love.
Galatians 5:6 ~ NIRV

Describe your faith. How does love flow from it?

*"They were trying to intimidate us into quitting.
They thought, 'They'll give up; they'll never finish it.'
I prayed, 'Give me strength.'"*

Nehemiah 6:9 ~ MSG

What does it look or feel like when God answers my prayer
for strength?

20_____

I will give you hidden treasures, riches stored in secret places, so that you may know that I am the Lord, the God of Israel, who summons you by name.
Isaiah 45:3 ~ NIV

What hidden treasures has your Father revealed to you?

_____
_____
_____
_____
_____
_____
_____
_____
_____
_____
_____
_____
_____
_____
_____
_____
_____
_____

3

20____

Be devoted to one another in love.
Honor one another above yourselves.

Romans 12:10 ~ NIV

Who has honored you through love and devotion? How has this changed your life?

_____

_____

_____

_____

_____

_____

_____

_____

_____

_____

_____

_____

_____

_____

_____

_____

_____

20____

Listen for God's voice in everything you do,
everywhere you go;
He's the one who will keep you on track.
Proverbs 3:6 ~ MSG

Do you hear the voice of God? How has He kept you on track spiritually?

_____

_____

_____

_____

_____

_____

_____

_____

_____

_____

_____

_____

_____

_____

_____

_____

5

20_____

 *March*

 *esus wept.*

John 11:35 ~ NIV

How does this verse touch you?

March

20____

on't worry about anything;
instead, pray about everything. Tell God what you
need, and thank Him for all He has done.

Philippians 4:6 ~ NLT

What are you anxious about? Today let God set you free
from worry.

_____

_____

_____

_____

_____

_____

_____

_____

_____

_____

_____

_____

_____

_____

_____

_____

_____

_____

20_____

*Where there is no vision, the people perish:
but he that keepeth the law, happy is he.*
Proverbs 29:18 ~ KJV

What is your vision for this year?

20_____

At that time Jesus went to a mountain to pray.
He spent the whole night in prayer to God.

Luke 6:12 ~ GW

Why do you need a quiet time with God each day?

20____

Enlarge the place of your tent,
stretch your tent curtains wide, do not hold back;
lengthen your cords, strengthen your stakes.
Isaiah 54:2 ~ NIV

How is God calling you to not hold back, but to push forward in expanding His kingdom?

_____

_____

_____

_____

_____

_____

_____

_____

_____

_____

_____

_____

_____

_____

_____

_____

_____

20_____

As a deer longs for a stream of cool water, so I long. For you, O God. I thirst for You, the living God. When can I go and worship in your presence?

Psalm 42:1-2 ~ GNT

Are you thirsty for God? Where do you go to be in His presence?

_____
_____
_____
_____
_____
_____
_____
_____
_____
_____
_____
_____
_____
_____
_____
_____
_____
_____

20_____

G̵od said to Noah, "This is how you are to build (the ark)" ... Noah did everything just as God commanded him.

Genesis 6: 15 , 22 ~ NIV

Is God commanding something from you? Are you doing everything just as He asked?

_____

_____

_____

_____

_____

_____

_____

_____

_____

_____

_____

_____

_____

_____

_____

_____

_____

20_____

In an abundance of counselors there is safety.

Proverbs 11:14 ~ NRSV

Are you surrounded by trustworthy Christian advisors?
How do you find safety in your relationships?

20_____

Be imitators of God, therefore, as dearly loved children and live a life of love, just as Christ loved us and gave Himself up for us as a fragrant offering and sacrifice to God.

Ephesians 5:1-2 NIV

Are you "Jesus with skin on"? Do others see you as a fragrant sacrifice to God?

$\mathcal{M}$arch

20_____

$\mathcal{W}$e walk by faith, not sight.
2 Corinthians 5:7 ~ NRSV

How are you walking by faith and not by sight?

20_____

Cast your cares on The Lord and He will sustain you; He will never let the righteous fall.
Psalm 55:22 ~ NIV

Spend some time writing out your cares to God!

*If it is possible, as far as it depends on you,
live at peace with everyone.*

Romans 12:18 ~ NIV

Do you live in peace with everyone? Write a prayer for peace in your life!

_____

_____

_____

_____

_____

_____

_____

_____

_____

_____

_____

_____

_____

_____

_____

_____

_____

20_____

*May the words of my mouth and
the meditations of my heart be pleasing in your sight,
O Lord, my rock and my redeemer.*

Psalm 19:14 ~ NIV

Are your words pleasing to God ? Confess if needed! Share how
God is your rock and refuge.

Plans fail for a lack of counsel,
but with many advisers they succeed.

Proverbs 15:22 ~ NIV

Who in your circle of friends gives support, courage, and love?

20____

*e kind to one another, tenderhearted, forgiving
one another, as God in Christ forgave you.*

Ephesians 4:32 ~ ESV

Who is God calling you to be tender-hearted to?

March 20

20_____

We do not try to please people,
but to please God, who tests our motives.
1 Thessalonians 2:4 ~ GNT

Write a commitment prayer detailing how you plan to please God.

_____
_____
_____
_____
_____
_____
_____
_____
_____
_____
_____
_____
_____
_____
_____
_____
_____

20____

Let the beauty of The Lord our God be upon us,
and establish the work for us;
yes, establish the work of our hands.

Psalm 90:17 ~ NKJV

How is the beauty of Lord upon you?

 arch

20_____

While it was still night, way before dawn he got up and went out to a secluded spot and prayed.

Mark 1:35 ~ MSG

Where is your secluded spot to pray?

20_____

*He makes me lie down in green pastures,
He leads me beside quite waters.*

Psalm 23:2 ~ NIV

Describe your favorite quiet place to be with God.

*B*ecause he has set his love upon me,
therefore I will deliver him; I will set him on high,
because he has known My name.

Psalm 91:14 ~ NKJV

How do you set Christ on high in your life?

_____
_____
_____
_____
_____
_____
_____
_____
_____
_____
_____
_____
_____
_____
_____
_____
_____

20_____

Be cheerful no matter what; pray all the time;
thank God no matter what happens.

1 Thessalonians 5:16-18 ~ MSG

Write about a time when you had to be cheerful while waiting on
God's answer.

March 26

20_____

ray for the peace of Jerusalem!
Psalm 126:6 ~ NIV

Write a prayer of peace for Jerusalem.

20____

From now on I'm alert day and night to the prayers offered at this place.

2 Chronicles 7:15 ~ MSG

How is God calling you to be alert day and night?

20_____

My requests have all been granted,
my prayers are answered.

Psalm 6:9 ~ MSG

Write about a time when God answered your prayers.

_____
_____
_____
_____
_____
_____
_____
_____
_____
_____
_____
_____
_____
_____

20____

here was also a prophet, Anna, the daughter of Penuel, of the tribe of Asher. She was very old; she had lived with her husband seven years after her marriage, and then was a widow until she was eighty-four. She never left the temple but worshiped night and day, fasting and praying.

Luke 2:36-37 ~ NIV

Describe Anna's calling (verse 37). What aspects of prayer and fasting is God calling you to?

20_____

I have heard your prayers,
I have seen your tears; surely I will heal you.

2 Kings 20:5 ~ NKJV

What healing are you praying for?

20_____

*reat my prayers as sweet incenses rising;
my raised hands are my evening prayers.*

Psalm 141:2 ~ MSG

Make a list of your prayer requests, and raise your hands to
Jesus!

Spring

20_____

*E*very day He was teaching in the temple complex. The chief priests, the scribes, and the leaders of the people were looking for a way to destroy Him.

Luke 19:47 ~ HCSB

Try to put yourself in Jesus' shoes! How would you feel if the very people you were trying to help were trying to have you killed?

hen Satan entered into Judas, called Iscariot, who was of the number of the twelve. He went away and conferred with the chief priests and officers how he might betray Him to them.

Luke 22:3-4 ~ ESV

Are you aware of Satan's presence? How sure are you of Christ's victory over him?

3

 April

20_____

He took bread, gave thanks and broke it, and gave it to them, saying, "This is my body given for you; do this in remembrance of me."

Luke 22:19 ~ NIV

How do you remember Christ's death?

20_____

*I will lift up the cup of salvation and call
on the name of the Lord. I will fulfill my vows to
the Lord in the presence of all His people.*
                              Psalm 116:13-14 ~ NIV

Have you ever made vows to the Lord that he is asking you to
fulfill?

_____

_____

_____

_____

_____

_____

_____

_____

_____

_____

_____

_____

_____

_____

_____

_____

_____

_____

20_____

"*My soul is overwhelmed with sorrow
to the point of death,*" *he said to them.
"Stay here and keep watch."

Mark 14:34 ~ NIV

What have been some of your overwhelming times? How did
God lead you through them?

_____

_____

_____

_____

_____

_____

_____

_____

_____

_____

_____

_____

_____

_____

_____

_____

20_____

*H*e said, *"Abba, Father! All things are possible for you. Take this cup away from me. Nevertheless, not what I will, but what you will."*

Mark 14: 36 ~ HCSB

What is God asking you to take out of your life now?

_____
_____
_____
_____
_____
_____
_____
_____
_____
_____
_____
_____
_____
_____
_____
_____
_____
_____
_____

20_____

eter said, "Man, I don't know what you're talking about." At that very moment, the last word hardly off his lips, a rooster crowed.

Luke 22:60 ~ MSG

How have you denied Christ? Spend some time writing a prayer of confession.

20_____

For God so loved the world that He gave His one and only Son, that whoever believes in Him shall not perish but have eternal life.

John 3:16 ~ NIV

Has there been a time when you have believed in Jesus and placed your trust in Him?

20_____

May the God of hope fill you with all joy and
peace as you trust in Him, so that you may overflow
with hope by the power of the Holy Sprit.
Romans 15:13 ~ NIV

How has trusting in God brought you joy and peace?

20_____

You are the light of the world-like a city on a hilltop that cannot be hidden.

Matthew 5: 14 ~ NLT

How are you being a light in your city?

_____
_____
_____
_____
_____
_____
_____
_____
_____
_____
_____
_____
_____
_____
_____
_____

20_____

*For wisdom will enter your heart,
and knowledge will be pleasant to your soul.*
Proverbs 2:10 ~ NIV

In what ways have you dedicated your life to spiritual growth?

20_____

*But I tell you, love your enemies
and pray for those who persecute you.*
Matthew 5:44 ~ NIV

How does this verse call you to love your enemies graciously?

_____

_____

_____

_____

_____

_____

_____

_____

_____

_____

_____

_____

_____

_____

_____

_____

_____

20_____

he Spirit and the bride say, "Come!"
And let the one who hears say, "Come!"
Let the one who is thirsty come; and let the one who
wishes take the free gift of the water of life.

Revelation 22:17 ~ NIV

How is Jesus calling you to come to Him?

20_____

$\mathcal{D}$o not conform to the pattern of this world,
but be transformed by the renewing of your mind.
Then you will be able to test and approve what God's
will is~ His good, pleasing and perfect will.

Romans 12:2 ~ NIV

What patterns in this world are you tempted to conform to?

_____

_____

_____

_____

_____

_____

_____

_____

_____

_____

_____

_____

_____

_____

_____

20_____

Enter His gates with thanksgiving and His courts with praise; give thanks to Him and praise His name.
Psalm 100:4 ~ NIV

Write a prayer of thanksgiving to God!

20_____

We give thanks to you, O God, we give thanks to you! We proclaim how great you are and tell of the wonderful things You have done.

Psalm: 75:1 ~ GNT

With whom do you share the great and wonderful things God has done in your life?

_____

_____

_____

_____

_____

_____

_____

_____

_____

_____

_____

_____

_____

_____

_____

_____

_____

_____

20_____

herefore, as God's chosen people, holy and dearly loved, clothe yourselves with compassion, kindness, humility, gentleness and patience.

Colossians 3:12 ~ NIV

When people look at you, what Christ-like qualities could they catch in you?

20_____

nyone who does not provide for their relatives, and especially for their own household, has denied the faith and is worse than an unbeliever.

1 Timothy 5:8 ~ NIV

How are you putting your family first? What kind of legacy do you want your family to remember you for?

_____

_____

_____

_____

_____

_____

_____

_____

_____

_____

_____

_____

_____

_____

_____

_____

_____

20____

A cheerful heart is good medicine,
but a crushed spirit dries up the bones.

Proverbs 17:22 ~ NIV

Can you laugh at yourself? List some ways you can show a cheerful heart.

_____

_____

_____

_____

_____

_____

_____

_____

_____

_____

_____

_____

_____

_____

_____

_____

_____

20_____

peak up for the people who have no voice,
for the rights of all the down-and-outers.
Speak out for justice!
Stand up for the poor and destitute!

Proverbs 31:8-9 ~ MSG

How can your voice make a difference for those less fortunate?

20____

Love never gives up, never loses faith, is always hopeful, and endures through every circumstance.
1 Corinthians 13:7 ~ NLT-

How is God encouraging you to exercise this kind of love?

20____

*ut Ruth replied, "Don't urge me to leave you
or to turn back from you. Where you go I will go,
and where you stay I will stay.
Your people will be my people and your God my God."*
Ruth 1:16 ~ NIV

For whom do you have this kind of devotion?

_____

_____

_____

_____

_____

_____

_____

_____

_____

_____

_____

_____

_____

_____

_____

_____

_____

_____

20_____

he woman was convinced. She saw that the tree was beautiful and its fruit looked delicious, and she wanted the wisdom it would give her. So she took some of the fruit and ate it. Then she gave some to her husband, who was with her, and he ate it, too.

Genesis 3:6 ~ NLT

How do you overcome temptation through God's power?

20_____

If we confess our sins,
He is faithful and just and will forgive us our sins
and purify us from all unrighteousness.

1 John 1:9 ~ NIV

Do you have sin in your life that you need to confess to God?

20____

*The Lord is good, a refuge in times of trouble.
He cares for those who trust in Him.*

Nahum 1:7 ~ NIV

How has the Lord been your refuge in times of trouble?

20_____

You have searched me, Lord,
and You know when I sit and when I rise;
You perceive my thoughts from afar.

Psalm 139:1-2 ~ NIV

How does this verse encourage you?

20____

Worry can rob you of happiness,
but kind words will cheer you up.

Proverbs 12:25 ~ GNT

Journal about a time when kind words cheered you up.

20_____

I am my beloved's and my beloved is mine;
he grazes among the lilies.

Song of Solomon 6:3 ~ ESV

When you hear that you are God's beloved, how does this encourage you?

_____

_____

_____

_____

_____

_____

_____

_____

_____

_____

_____

_____

_____

_____

_____

_____

_____

_____

20____

*After six days Jesus took Peter, James and John
with Him and led them up a high mountain,
where they were all alone.
There He was transfigured before them.*

Mark 9:2 ~ NIV

What is your favorite memory of spending time with your
best friends?

_____

_____

_____

_____

_____

_____

_____

_____

_____

_____

_____

_____

_____

_____

_____

_____

20_____

When all kinds of trials and temptations crowd into your lives, my brothers, don't resent them as intruders, but welcome them as friends!

James 1:2 ~ Phillips

Think back to a trial or temptation in your life. What lesson did you learn from that experience?

_____

_____

_____

_____

_____

_____

_____

_____

_____

_____

_____

_____

_____

_____

_____

_____

_____

_____

_____

_____

_____

20____

Cast all your anxiety on Him because He cares for you.

1 Peter 5:7 ~ NIV

Are you worried, anxious, or fearful? Give your concerns to
Jesus in a written prayer. Do you believe that He cares for you?

20_____

Jesus said, "If you knew the gift of God and who it is that asks you for a drink, you would have asked him and he would have given you living water."

John 4:10 ~ NIV
(Samaritan Woman at the well)

Are you thirsty for God? Are you in need of living water?

_____
_____
_____
_____
_____
_____
_____
_____
_____
_____
_____
_____
_____
_____
_____
_____

20_____

God thunders wondrously with His voice;
He does great things that we cannot comprehend.

Job 37:5 ~ ESV

Describe the last time Christ amazed you.

orgive us our sins, for we also forgive everyone who sins against us. And lead us not into temptation.

Luke 11:4 ~ NIV

What kind of temptations have you struggled with while walking by God's side?

20_____

I consider that our present sufferings are not worth comparing with the glory that will be revealed in us.
Romans 8:18 ~ NIV

List what you're going through and how you're hurting.
Ask God to deliver you through this.

20____

When Jesus saw His mother there, and the disciple
whom He loved standing nearby, He said to her,
"Woman, here is your son," and to the disciple,
"Here is your mother."
From that time on, this disciple took her into his home.

John 19: 26-27 ~ NIV

What responsibilities has Christ given you?

_____

_____

_____

_____

_____

_____

_____

_____

_____

_____

_____

_____

_____

_____

_____

20_____

imon Peter answered,
"You are the Messiah, the Son of the living God."
Matthew 16:16 ~ NIV

How has the Messiah, the King of Kings, become your Living God?

_____

_____

_____

_____

_____

_____

_____

_____

_____

_____

_____

_____

_____

_____

_____

_____

_____

20_____

Brothers, do not be children in your thinking. Be infants in evil, but in your thinking be mature.
1 Corinthians 14:20 ~ ESV

Who is the most mature believer you know? What attributes set him or her apart?

_____

_____

_____

_____

_____

_____

_____

_____

_____

_____

_____

_____

_____

_____

_____

_____

_____

_____

20____

rust in Him at all times, you people;
pour out your hearts to Him, for God is our refuge.

Psalm 62:8 ~ NIV

Refuge means shelter, safety, sanctuary, and our hideaway.
Which word describes how God is your refuge?

_____

_____

_____

_____

_____

_____

_____

_____

_____

_____

_____

_____

_____

_____

_____

_____

_____

20_____

Be of good courage, and He shall strengthen your heart, all you that hope in the Lord.

Psalm 31:24 ~ KJV

As you have placed your hope in the Lord, how has that strengthened your heart?

_____

_____

_____

_____

_____

_____

_____

_____

_____

_____

_____

_____

_____

_____

_____

20_____

Rejoice in the Lord always,
I will say it again: Rejoice!

Philippians 4:4 ~ NIV

Rejoice in the Lord through writing a prayer of thanksgiving.

20_____

*his is my command- be strong and courageous!
Do not be afraid or discouraged. For the Lord your God
is with you wherever you go.*

Joshua 1:9 ~ NLT

Who do you consider to be the strongest and most courageous
person?

20____

*B*lessed are the meek,
for they will inherit the earth.

Matthew 5:5 ~ NIV

Jesus was powerful, but He was gentle. How will you follow in His footsteps?

_____

_____

_____

_____

_____

_____

_____

_____

_____

_____

_____

_____

_____

_____

_____

_____

_____

_____

_____

May 14

20_____

$\mathcal{K}$now therefore that the Lord your God is God;
He is the faithful God, keeping His covenant of love
to a thousand generations of those who love Him and
keep His commandments.

Deuteronomy 7:9 ~ NIV

How have you experienced God's faithfulness?

_____
_____
_____
_____
_____
_____
_____
_____
_____
_____
_____
_____
_____
_____
_____
_____
_____

20_____

*he Lord also will be a refuge for the oppressed,
a refuge in times of trouble.*

Psalm 9:9 ~ KJV

How have you experienced help from the Lord in times of
trouble?

20_____

hese things I have spoken to you, that my joy may be in you, and that your joy may be full.

John 15:11 ~ ESV

How do you express His joy that is in you?

_____
_____
_____
_____
_____
_____
_____
_____
_____
_____
_____
_____
_____
_____
_____
_____
_____
_____

20_____

We love Him, because He first loved us.
1 John 4:19 ~ KJV

Express your love for God.

_____

_____

_____

_____

_____

_____

_____

_____

_____

_____

_____

_____

_____

_____

_____

_____

_____

_____

20_____

Evening, and morning, and at noon, will I pray, and cry aloud: and He shall hear my voice.

Psalm 55:17 ~ KJV

Do you believe God hears your voice? If so, why is it so hard to pray more often?

_____

_____

_____

_____

_____

_____

_____

_____

_____

_____

_____

_____

_____

_____

_____

_____

_____

20____

Let us hold fast the profession of our faith without wavering; (for He is faithful that promised).
                                                    Hebrew 10:23 ~ KJV

How have you been patiently waiting for His will?

May

20_____

And they went out,
and preached that men should repent.

Mark 6:12 ~ KJV

Repentance is what leads to transformation in our spiritual
journey. Spend some time writing a repentance prayer to
your Savior.

_____

_____

_____

_____

_____

_____

_____

_____

_____

_____

_____

_____

_____

_____

_____

20_____

*And also that every man should eat and drink,
and enjoy the good of all his labor,
it is the gift of God.*

Ecclesiastes 3:13 ~ KJV

How has God lavished on you?

20_____

How ow blessed is the man who has made
the Lord his trust.

Psalm 40:4 ~ NASB

How are you experiencing our Lord lifting your heart as you
trust in Him?

_____

_____

_____

_____

_____

_____

_____

_____

_____

_____

_____

_____

_____

_____

_____

_____

_____

20_____

*He refreshes my soul. He guides me along the right
Paths for his name's sake.*

Psalm 23:3 ~ NIV

How do you need Jesus to refresh your soul? Let him guide your
thoughts.

_____

_____

_____

_____

_____

_____

_____

_____

_____

_____

_____

_____

_____

_____

_____

_____

_____

20_____

*I am the Alpha and the Omega,
the First and the Last, the Beginning and the End.*

Revelation 22: 13 ~ NIV

Which attribute or description means the most to you and why?

20_____

*Exalt the Lord our God, and worship at His holy
mountain, for the Lord our God is holy.*

Psalm 99:9 ~ NASB

Is rejoicing a way of life for you? How do you celebrate the one
worthy of your praise?

_____

_____

_____

_____

_____

_____

_____

_____

_____

_____

_____

_____

_____

_____

_____

_____

_____

_____

20_____

*sought The Lord, and He heard me,
and delivered me from all my fears.*

Psalm 34:4 ~ KJV

Are you struggling with any fears? Ask Him to deliver you from them.

20_____

Better to eat dry crust with peace of mind
than have a banquet in a house full of trouble.

Proverbs 17:1 ~ GNT

What does this verse mean to you?

_____

_____

_____

_____

_____

_____

_____

_____

_____

_____

_____

_____

_____

_____

_____

_____

_____

May *28*

20_____

Therefore, having been justified by faith,
we have peace with God through our Lord Jesus Christ.
Romans 5:1 ~ NASB

Describe your peace with God.

_____
_____
_____
_____
_____
_____
_____
_____
_____
_____
_____
_____
_____
_____

20____

You, God, are awesome in your sanctuary;
the God of Israel gives power and strength
to his people. Praise God!

Psalm 68:35 ~ NIV

Spend some time praising God for His power and strength
revealed in His sanctuary.

_____
_____
_____
_____
_____
_____
_____
_____
_____
_____
_____
_____
_____
_____
_____

20_____

Praise God, everybody! Applaud God, all people!

Psalm 117:1 ~ MSG

What type of applause is God looking for?

_____

_____

_____

_____

_____

_____

_____

_____

_____

_____

_____

_____

_____

_____

_____

_____

_____

_____

_____

20____

*ear not, I have redeemed you;
I have called you by name; you are mine.*

Isaiah 43:1 ~ NKJV

How does belonging to Him give you courage?

_____

_____

_____

_____

_____

_____

_____

_____

_____

_____

_____

_____

_____

_____

_____

_____

_____

_____

_____

20____

Your Kingdom come,
your will be done,
on earth as it is in heaven.

Matthew 6:10 ~ ESV

What is God asking you to surrender to Him?
Allow His will to be done.

20_____

hey recognized him as the same man who used to sit begging at the temple gate called Beautiful, and they were filled with wonder and amazement at what had happened to him. (Peter Heals a Lame Begger)

Acts 3:10~NIV

Describe a time when you witnessed a miracle.

_____

_____

_____

_____

_____

_____

_____

_____

_____

_____

_____

_____

_____

_____

_____

_____

20_____

"*Because he has set his love upon me,
therefore I will deliver him, I will set him on high,
because he has known my name.*

Psalm 91:14 ~ NKJV

Write a thank you note to God for knowing your name!

20_____

he Lord is my rock, my fortress and my deliverer;
my God is my rock, in whom I take refuge, my shield
and the horn of my salvation, my stronghold.
Psalm 18:2 ~ NIV

Recount how the Lord has been your rock and fortress.

20_____

"*For I know the plans I have for you,*"
declares the Lord, "plans to prosper you and not to
harm you, plans to give you hope and a future."
Jeremiah 29:11 ~ NIV

In what ways are you needing hope for your future?

_____
_____
_____
_____
_____
_____
_____
_____
_____
_____
_____
_____
_____
_____
_____
_____
_____
_____
_____

20_____

hen have them make a sanctuary for me, and I will dwell among them. Make this tabernacle and all its furnishings exactly like the pattern I will show you.
Exodus 25:8-9 ~ NIV

What is the most beautiful cathedral you have ever seen? Describe its beauty.

_____

_____

_____

_____

_____

_____

_____

_____

_____

_____

_____

_____

_____

_____

_____

_____

_____

_____

 une

20_____

I will sing to Yahweh throughout my life; I will sing praise to my God while I remain alive.

Psalm 104:33 ~ LEB

How could the commitment of the psalmist be a model for your life?

20_____

eace I leave with you; my peace I give to you.
Not as the world gives do I give.

John 14:27 ~ ESV

How do you find peace in times of trouble?

20_____

et I will rejoice in the Lord, I will be joyful in God my Savior.

Habakkuk 3:18 ~ NIV

Have you ever felt like not rejoicing? Describe a time when you chose to rejoice. Describe how you felt!

20_____

he son is the image of the invisible God,
the firstborn over all creation

Colossians 1:15 ~ NIV

Why is it so important to establish the identity of Jesus as the image of the invisible God?

20_____

*he Lord is good to those whose hope is in Him,
to the one who seeks Him.*

Lamentations 3:25 ~ NIV

What good things are happening as a result of hoping in and seeking him?

20____

But when you pray, go into your room,
close the door and pray to your Father, who is unseen.
Then your Father, who sees what is done in secret,
will reward you.

Matthew 6:6 ~ NIV

What kind of tender, intimate moments have you had with
your Father?

_____

_____

_____

_____

_____

_____

_____

_____

_____

_____

_____

_____

_____

_____

_____

_____

_____

20____

Wait for the Lord; be strong and take heart
and wait for the Lord.

Psalm 27:14 ~ NIV

What are you waiting and longing for? Take heart and wait on
the Lord!

20_____

And Gideon said to him, "Please, sir, if the Lord is with us, why then has all this happened to us? And where are all his wonderful deeds that our fathers recounted to us, saying, 'Did not the Lord bring us up from Egypt?' But now the Lord has forsaken us and given us into the hand of Midian."

Judges 6:13 ~ ESV

When trauma enters your life, do you believe that God has forsaken you or that God has an amazing plan?

_____

_____

_____

_____

_____

_____

_____

_____

_____

_____

_____

_____

_____

_____

20_____

$\mathcal{D}$o not let your hearts be troubled.
You believe in God; believe also in Me.

John 14:1 ~ NIV

What are your troubles? Are you believing in God to release
your heart from these?

_____

_____

_____

_____

_____

_____

_____

_____

_____

_____

_____

_____

_____

_____

_____

_____

_____

20_____

But seek ye first the kingdom of God,
and his righteousness; and all these things shall be
added unto you.

Matthew 6:33 ~ NJVA

Where is your favorite place to have your personal quiet time?

20_____

The thief does not come except to steal, and to kill, and to destroy. I have come that they may have life, and that they may have it more abundantly.

John 10:10 ~ NKJV

How have you experienced a more abundant life in Christ?

_____

_____

_____

_____

_____

_____

_____

_____

_____

_____

_____

_____

_____

_____

_____

_____

20_____

I am leaving you with a gift-peace of mind and heart. And the peace I give is a gift the world cannot give. So don't be troubled or afraid.

John 14:27 ~ NLT

How has the Lord given you the gift of peace for your mind and soul?

_____

_____

_____

_____

_____

_____

_____

_____

_____

_____

_____

_____

_____

_____

_____

_____

_____

_____

20_____

ut on my yoke and learn from me.
For I am gentle and humble in heart
and you will find rest for your souls.

Matthew 11:29 ~ Phillips

What kind of rest do you need?

_____

_____

_____

_____

_____

_____

_____

_____

_____

_____

_____

_____

_____

_____

_____

_____

_____

_____

20____

The name of the Lord is strong Tower: the righteous runneth into it, and is safe.

Proverbs 18:10 ~ KJV

Share a moment that you experienced God's protection.

20_____

"*Put into action the word I covenanted with you when you left Egypt. I'm living and breathing among you right now. Don't be timid. Don't hold back.*"

Haggai 2:5 ~ MSG

How is the Holy Spirit telling you to move right now? What is the next step you need to take?

_____

_____

_____

_____

_____

_____

_____

_____

_____

_____

_____

_____

_____

_____

_____

_____

20_____

And yet, O Lord, you are our Father.
We are the clay, and you are the potter. We all are
formed by your hand.

Isaiah 64:8 ~ NLT

Do you trust Him as He holds you in His hands while shaping you?

20_____

Taste and see that the Lord is good;
blessed is the one who takes refuge in him.

Psalm 34:8 ~ NIV

Describe how the Lord has been good to you!

20____

You shall have no other gods before me.
Deuteronomy 5:7 ~ ESV

Spend some time searching your heart for idols, and write a prayer of confession below.

_____
_____
_____
_____
_____
_____
_____
_____
_____
_____
_____
_____
_____
_____
_____
_____
_____
_____

20_____

Better is a handful of quietness than two hands
full of toil and a striving after wind.

Ecclesiastes 4:6 ~ ESV

What brings you true quietness?

20_____

No longer do I call you servants, for the servant does not know what his master is doing; but I have called you friends, for all that I have heard from my Father I have made known to you.

John 15:15 ~ ESV

In what ways is Jesus your friend?

_____

_____

_____

_____

_____

_____

_____

_____

_____

_____

_____

_____

_____

_____

_____

_____

_____

_____

20_____

In peace I will lie down and sleep, for you alone, Lord, make me dwell in safety.

Psalm 4:8 ~ NIV

How has God's safety freed you from anxiety?

20____

*$\mathcal{M}$y soul, wait silently for God alone,
for my expectation is from Him.*

Psalm 62:5 ~ NKJV

How does this verse challenge you spiritually?

_____

_____

_____

_____

_____

_____

_____

_____

_____

_____

_____

_____

_____

_____

_____

_____

20_____

For the grace of God that brings salvation has appeared to all men.

Titus 2:11 ~ NKJV

Describe the moment when salvation appeared to you.

20_____

Ah Lord God! Behold, thou hast made the heaven and the earth by Thy great power and stretched out arm, and there is nothing too hard for Thee.

Jeremiah 32:17 ~ KJV

What are your difficult circumstances? Are you believing that nothing is too hard for God?

Summer

20_____

*But you remain the same,
and your years will never end.*

Psalm 102:27 ~ NIV

There is no end with God! How have you experienced His
consistent presence?

20_____

he Lord is with me: He is my helper. I look in triumph on my enemies.

Psalm 118:7 ~NIV

How are you trusting God to defeat the source of evil?

_____

_____

_____

_____

_____

_____

_____

_____

_____

_____

_____

_____

_____

_____

_____

_____

_____

_____

20_____

It is better to take refuge in the Lord than to trust in humans.

Psalm 118:8 ~ NIV

How is the Lord your refuge?

20____

And there before me was the glory of the God of Israel, as in the vision I had seen in the plain.

Ezekiel 8:4 ~ NIV

Describe a moment you saw a glimpse of God's glory.

20_____

For where your treasure is,
there your heart will be also.

Luke 12:34 ~ NIV

What do you treasure most?

20_____

Call upon Me in the day of trouble;
I will deliver you, and you shall glorify Me.

Psalm 50:15 ~ NKJV

Describe a moment when you called out to God and He delivered you from your trouble. Did you give Him glory?

_____

_____

_____

_____

_____

_____

_____

_____

_____

_____

_____

_____

_____

_____

_____

_____

_____

_____

20_____

*"Don't be afraid." He said,
"Take courage. I am here!"*

Matthew 14:27 ~ NLT

How is Jesus calling you to have more courage?

20_____

I *am the Lord, your Holy One,*
  Israel's Creator, your King.

Isaiah 43:15 ~ NIV

How has Jesus been your Lord, your Holy One, your Creator, and your King?

_____

_____

_____

_____

_____

_____

_____

_____

_____

_____

_____

_____

_____

_____

_____

_____

_____

_____

20_____

But Jesus Himself would often slip away to the wilderness and pray.

Luke 5:16 ~ AMP

How have you followed the example of Jesus in slipping away to be with God?

_____

_____

_____

_____

_____

_____

_____

_____

_____

_____

_____

_____

_____

_____

_____

_____

_____

_____

The one who loves Me will be loved by My Father. I also will love him and will reveal Myself to him.

John 14:21 ~ HCSB

What does Jesus say is a prerequisite for Him to reveal Himself?

"Come, follow me," Jesus said, "and I will send you out to fish for people."
At once they left their nets and followed Him.
Matthew 4:19-20 ~ NIV

What is Jesus asking you to drop in order to follow Him more closely?

20_____

In the day when I cried out, You answered me, and made me bold with strength in my soul.

Psalm 138:3 ~ NKJV

How has God given you confidence to face your trials?

20_____

GOD's Judgment Day is near for all the godless
nations. As you have done, it will be done to you...
"But not so on Mount Zion—there's respite there!
a safe and holy place!..."

Obadiah 1:15-18 ~ MSG

Where is the safe and holy place that God has set aside for you?
If you don't know, ask Him.

always thank my God as I remember you in my prayers, because I hear about your love for all His holy people and your faith in the Lord Jesus.

Philemon 4-5 ~ NIV

Who are you remembering in your prayers?

20_____

He rescues and He saves; He performs signs and wonders in the heavens and on the earth. He has rescued Daniel from the power of the lions.

Daniel 6:27 ~ NIV

What signs and wonders have you seen? How has He rescued you?

_____

_____

_____

_____

_____

_____

_____

_____

_____

_____

_____

_____

_____

_____

_____

_____

_____

_____

_____

20_____

his is My command: Love each other.
John 15:17 ~ NIV

How are you modeling this command?

20_____

Every word of God is flawless;
He is a shield to those who take refuge in Him.

Proverbs 30:5 ~ NIV

How has God been your shield and a place of refuge?

_____

_____

_____

_____

_____

_____

_____

_____

_____

_____

_____

_____

_____

_____

_____

20_____

Whoever wants to be my disciple must deny themselves and take up their cross daily and follow me.
Luke 9:23 ~ NIV

What does it mean, as a disciple, to take up your cross daily?

_____
_____
_____
_____
_____
_____
_____
_____
_____
_____
_____
_____
_____
_____
_____
_____

20_____

*O*verhearing what they said, Jesus told him,
"Don't be afraid; just believe."

Mark 5:36 ~ NIV

Do you struggle with fear? What is one area in your life where
God is asking you to not be afraid and just believe Him?

20_____

he counsel of the Lord stands forever,
the thoughts and plans of His heart
through all generations.

Psalm 33:11 ~ AMP

God's counsel stands forever! How does the fact that God's
counsel stands forever challenge the way you're living?

_____

_____

_____

_____

_____

_____

_____

_____

_____

_____

_____

_____

_____

_____

_____

_____

_____

_____

20____

*am concerned for you and will look on you with
favor; you will be plowed and sown.*

Ezekiel 36:9 ~ NIV

What does this verse say about how God looks at us?

_____
_____
_____
_____
_____
_____
_____
_____
_____
_____
_____
_____
_____
_____
_____
_____
_____

20_____

A man's heart plans his way,
but the Lord directs his steps.

Proverbs 16:9 ~ NKJV

How has the Lord directed your steps to grow closer to Him?

20_____

*E*ven though I walk through the darkest valley,
I will fear no evil, for you are with me;
your rod and your staff, they comfort me.

Psalm 23:4 ~ NIV

Reflect through journaling about a time when God walked you
through a valley.

_____

_____

_____

_____

_____

_____

_____

_____

_____

_____

_____

_____

_____

_____

_____

_____

For though I am free from all, I have made myself
a servant to all, that I might win more of them.

1 Corinthians 9:19 ~ ESV

How is God reaching the world through you?

20_____

hank you! Everything in me says "Thank you!"
Angels listen as I sing my thanks. I kneel in worship
facing your holy temple and say it again: "Thank you!"
Psalm 138:1 ~ MSG

How do you need to say "Thank you" to God?

_____

_____

_____

_____

_____

_____

_____

_____

_____

_____

_____

_____

_____

_____

_____

In my distress I called to the Lord, and He answered me. From deep in the realm of the dead I called for help, and you listened to my cry.

Jonah 2:2 ~ NIV

Who listens to your cries? When was the last time you cried out to God?

_____

_____

_____

_____

_____

_____

_____

_____

_____

_____

_____

_____

_____

_____

_____

_____

_____

20_____

*herefore confess your sins to each other
so that you may be healed. The prayer of
a righteous person is powerful and effective.*
James 5:16 ~ NIV

List prayers both big and small that God has answered for you.

20_____

rust in the Lord forever,
For in YAH, the Lord, is everlasting strength.
Isaiah 26:4 ~ NKJV

When was the last time your trust in God challenged you?

20_____

Devote yourselves to prayer
with an alert mind and a thankful heart.

Colossians 4:2 ~ NLT

What is the meaning of devote? How is God calling you to live out this verse?

_____

_____

_____

_____

_____

_____

_____

_____

_____

_____

_____

_____

_____

_____

20_____

At Gibeon the Lord appeared to Solomon during the night in a dream, and God said, "Ask for whatever you want me to give you."

1 Kings 3:5 ~ NIV

How has the Lord been generous to you?

20____

hank God! He deserves your thanks.
His love never quits.

Psalm 136:1 ~ MSG

Explain how His love has never quit.

20_____

He will wipe away every tear from their eyes, and there will be no more death or sorrow or crying or pain. All these things are gone forever.

Revelation 21:4 ~ NLT

How does this promise encourage you?

_____
_____
_____
_____
_____
_____
_____
_____
_____
_____
_____
_____
_____
_____
_____
_____
_____
_____
_____

20_____

God's strong name is our help,
the same God who made heaven and earth.

Psalm 124:8 ~ MSG

How does this verse help you depend on His help?

_____

_____

_____

_____

_____

_____

_____

_____

_____

_____

_____

_____

_____

_____

_____

_____

20_____

*or you, Lord, make my lamp shine;
my God enlightens my darkness.*

2 Samuel 22:29 ~ ISV

What problem are you currently facing in which you need God
to give you light?

20_____

That's why, for Christ sake, I delight in weaknesses, in insults, in hardships, in persecutions, in difficulties. For when I am weak, then I am strong.
2 Corinthians 12:10 ~ NIV

Describe a time when you have been faced with a hardship and God has made you strong.

20_____

Thank you for your love,
thank you for your faithfulness;
most holy is your name, most holy is your Word.

Psalm 138:2 ~ MSG

How has God's love and faithfulness changed your life?

20_____

Keep this Book of the Law always on your lips; meditate on it day and night, so that you may be careful to do everything written in it. Then you will be prosperous and successful.

Joshua 1:8 ~ NIV

What does Joshua 1:8 mean to you?

_____

_____

_____

_____

_____

_____

_____

_____

_____

_____

_____

_____

_____

_____

_____

_____

She is a tree of life to those who take hold of her; those who hold her fast will be blessed.

Proverbs 3:18 ~ NIV

How have you taken hold of God's wisdom? How have you been blessed?

_____

_____

_____

_____

_____

_____

_____

_____

_____

_____

_____

_____

_____

_____

_____

_____

_____

_____

_____

20_____

"*Fear not:*
for, behold I bring you good tidings of great joy."
Luke 2:10 ~ KJV

No matter what your fears may be, He is saying to you right now, "Fear not." Why?

_____

_____

_____

_____

_____

_____

_____

_____

_____

_____

_____

_____

_____

_____

_____

_____

_____

20____

But I will restore you to health and heal your wounds, declares the Lord, because you are called an outcast, Zion for whom no one cares.
Jeremiah 30:17 ~ NIV

In what ways has the Lord restored and healed your wounds?

I have asked the Lord for one thing; one thing only do I want: to live in the Lord's house all my life, to marvel there at His goodness, and to ask for His guidance.

Psalm 27:4 GNT

Do you experience the same passion for God's presence? Why or why not?

_____

_____

_____

_____

_____

_____

_____

_____

_____

_____

_____

_____

_____

_____

_____

_____

_____

20_____

May you know more and more of grace and peace as your knowledge of God and Jesus our Lord grows deeper.

2 Peter 1:2 ~ Philips

Have you learned what grace is through growing in Christ? Describe what grace looks like in your life.

_____

_____

_____

_____

_____

_____

_____

_____

_____

_____

_____

_____

_____

_____

_____

_____

_____

_____

_____

20_____

The shepherds returned, glorifying and praising God for all the things they had heard and seen, which were just as they had been told.

Luke 2:20 ~ NIV

What have you seen God do that has caused you to praise Him?

20_____

O my God, I lift high your praise.
Thank God ~ He's so good. His love never quits!
Psalm 118:29 MSG

When have you experienced a love that never quits?

_____

_____

_____

_____

_____

_____

_____

_____

_____

_____

_____

_____

_____

_____

_____

20_____

"*Your Kingdom come, your will be done, on earth as it is in heaven.*"

Matthew 6:10 ~ NIV

How is God's will done in your life, as it is in heaven?

_____

_____

_____

_____

_____

_____

_____

_____

_____

_____

_____

_____

_____

_____

_____

_____

_____

_____

20_____

"*Give us today our daily bread.*"
Matthew 6:11 ~ NIV

How is God providing for your needs?

20_____

"*And forgive us our debts,
as we also have forgiven our debtors.*"

Matthew 6:12 ~ NIV

Are you harboring any bitterness or unforgiveness in
your heart? Explain your reasoning.

_____

_____

_____

_____

_____

_____

_____

_____

_____

_____

_____

_____

_____

_____

_____

_____

20_____

"*And lead us not into temptation,*
but deliver us from evil: For thine is the kingdom,
and the power, and the glory, forever. Amen"

Matthew 6:13 ~ KJV

Are you struggling with temptation? Ask God to deliver you from evil.

20_____

For my yoke is easy and my burden is light.
Matthew 11:30 ~ NIV

How have your burdens become lighter through knowing Jesus?

20____

Casting all your care upon him;
for he careth for you.

1 Peter 5:7 ~ KJV

How can Jesus care for all of your needs?

20_____

o mere man has ever seen, heard, or even imagined what wonderful things God has ready for those who love the Lord.

1 Corinthians 2:9 ~ TLB

What wonderful things has God done for you?

_____

_____

_____

_____

_____

_____

_____

_____

_____

_____

_____

_____

_____

_____

_____

_____

_____

"*The sons of Seir: Lotan, Shobal, Zibeon, Anah, Dishon, Ezer, and Dishan. The sons of Lotan: Hori and Hemam; and Lotan's sister was Timna.*"

1 Chronicles 1:38-39 ~ ESV

God knows every person by their name. Think back to a nameless face you saw today. Pray for them. How did that feel?

_____

_____

_____

_____

_____

_____

_____

_____

_____

_____

_____

_____

_____

_____

_____

_____

_____

_____

_____

20_____

In my Father's house are many mansions;
if it were not so, I would have told you.
John 14:2 ~ NIV

Describe heaven in your own words and what it means to you.

20_____

*Behold, I stand at the door and knock. If anyone
hears My voice and opens the door, I will come in to
him and dine with him, and he with Me.*

Revelation 3:20 ~ NKJV

When did Christ stand at your heart and knock? Did you open
the door?

_____

_____

_____

_____

_____

_____

_____

_____

_____

_____

_____

_____

_____

_____

_____

_____

_____

_____

20_____

*esus Christ is the same
yesterday and today and forever.*

Hebrews 13:8 ~ NIV

How has Christ been consistent in your life?

20_____

"*But whoever drinks the water I give them will never thirst. Indeed, the water I give them will become in them a spring of water welling up to eternal life.*"

John 4:14 ~ NIV

Are you thirsty? How can Jesus quench your thirst?

20_____

"I have told you these things, so that in Me you may have peace. In this world you will have trouble. But take heart! I have overcome the world."
John 16:33 ~ NIV

He invites you to bring your cares and burdens to Him. Take some time to list your burdens and cares, and ask God to give you peace.

_____

_____

_____

_____

_____

_____

_____

_____

_____

_____

_____

_____

_____

_____

_____

_____

_____

20_____

hen God said, "Take your son, your only son, whom you love - Isaac - and go to the region of Moriah. Sacrifice him there as a burnt offering on a mountain I will show you."

Genesis 22:2 ~ NIV

When has God called you to lay down your Isaac on an altar?

20_____

*Therefore, if anyone is in Christ, the new creation
has come: The old has gone, the new is here!*
2 Corinthians 5:17 ~ NIV

How does this verse give you hope?

20_____

hanks be to God for His indescribable gift!
2 Corinthians 9:15 ~ NKJV

How has the gift of Jesus changed your life?

30 August

20_____

Let the morning bring me words of Your unfailing love, for I have put my trust in You. Show me the way I should go, for to You I entrust my life.

Psalm 143:8 ~NIV

Is God asking you to do something that you are afraid to do?
What does it look like to trust Him to lead you?

_____

_____

_____

_____

_____

_____

_____

_____

_____

_____

_____

_____

_____

_____

_____

_____

20____

I have fought the good fight,
I have finished the race, I have kept the faith.
2 Timothy 4:7 ~ NIV

What would it mean for you to be able to say, "I have fought the good fight, I have finished the race, I have kept the faith"?

20_____

"*Behold, the virgin shall conceive and bear a son,
and they shall call His name Immanuel"
(which means, God with us.)*
Matthew 1:23 ~ESV

What are some ways you can think of that Jesus fulfilled the
meaning of Immanuel ?

_____

_____

_____

_____

_____

_____

_____

_____

_____

_____

_____

_____

_____

_____

_____

_____

_____

20_____

"Holy, holy, holy is the Lord Almighty;
the whole earth is full of His glory."

Isaiah 6:3 ~ NIV

What does it mean that the Lord is holy? How do you see the
earth full of His glory?

_____

_____

_____

_____

_____

_____

_____

_____

_____

_____

_____

_____

_____

_____

_____

_____

_____

_____

20_____

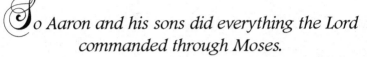

o Aaron and his sons did everything the Lord
commanded through Moses.

Leviticus 8:36 ~ NIV

Are you a follower of the Lord's commands? What is He
commanding you to do?

_____

_____

_____

_____

_____

_____

_____

_____

_____

_____

_____

_____

_____

_____

_____

_____

*E*ven the Spirit of truth; whom the world cannot
receive, because it seeth him not, neither knoweth him:
but ye know him; for he dwelleth with you,
and shall be in you. I will not leave you comfortless:
I will come to you.

John 14:17-18 ~ AKJV

Have you ever felt you were abandoned or living in isolation?
How does this verse give you great comfort?

20_____

*"On the day when I act," says the Lord Almighty,
"they will be my treasured possession."*

Malachi 3:17 ~ NIV

What is your treasured possession?

_____

_____

_____

_____

_____

_____

_____

_____

_____

_____

_____

_____

_____

_____

_____

_____

_____

20_____

So we fix our eyes not on what is seen,
but on what is unseen, since what is seen is temporary,
but what is unseen is eternal.

2 Corinthians 4:18 ~ NIV

How do you fix your sight on the eternal?

7 *September* 7

20_____

*L*et everything that has breath and every breath
of life praise the Lord! Praise the Lord! Hallelujah!
Psalm 150:6 ~ AMP

As you think about His greatness, praise Him with your words.

20____

But when the set time had fully come,
God send His Son, born of a woman,
born under the law, to redeem those under the law,
that we might receive adoption to sonship.
                                      Galatians 4:4-5 ~ NIV

In what ways would you like to say thank you to God for what
He has done?

_____
_____
_____
_____
_____
_____
_____
_____
_____
_____
_____
_____
_____
_____
_____
_____
_____
_____

20_____

*I have not stopped giving thanks for you,
remembering you in my prayers.*

Ephesians 1:16~ NIV

What lonely people can you think of right now? How can you
reach out to them?

_____

_____

_____

_____

_____

_____

_____

_____

_____

_____

_____

_____

_____

_____

_____

_____

_____

_____

20_____

*For the Son of Man came to seek
and save that which was lost.*

John 14:10 ~ AMP

Spend time thanking God for this wonderful and glorious hope.

20_____

For Christ did not send me to baptize, but to preach the gospel-not with wisdom and eloquence, lest the cross of Christ be emptied of its power.

1 Corinthians 1:17 ~ NIV

What is Paul's goal as he presents the gospel to the Corinthians?

_____

_____

_____

_____

_____

_____

_____

_____

_____

_____

_____

_____

_____

_____

_____

_____

_____

_____

September 12

20_____

Jesus answered, "I am the way and the truth and the life. No one comes to the Father except through me."

John 14:6 ~ NIV

What did Jesus mean when He said, "I am the way and the truth and the life"?

_____

_____

_____

_____

_____

_____

_____

_____

_____

_____

_____

_____

_____

_____

_____

_____

_____

_____

20_____

Love is patient, love is kind. It does not boast,
it is not proud. It does not dishonor others, it is not
self-seeking, it is not easily angered,
it keeps no record of wrongs.

1 Corinthians 13:4-5 ~ NIV

What actions of love does Paul list here?

_____

_____

_____

_____

_____

_____

_____

_____

_____

_____

_____

_____

_____

_____

_____

20_____

*And let us consider how we may spur one another
on toward love and good deeds.*

Hebrews 10:24 ~ NIV

Have you experienced a community that spurs you on toward
love and good deeds? List some of those deeds. Think of a time
when you could have acted but didn't. How would you do it
differently next time?

_____

_____

_____

_____

_____

_____

_____

_____

_____

_____

_____

_____

_____

_____

_____

20_____

Therefore go and make disciples of all nations,
baptizing them in the name of the Father
and of the Son and of the Holy Spirit.
Matthew 28:19 ~ NIV

Are you helping to fulfill the Great Commission? Describe your
most memorable story!

 eptember

20_____

*L̲isten, dear friends, to God's truth, bend your
ears to what I tell you. I'm chewing on the morsel of
a proverb; I'll let you in on the sweet old truths, stories
we heard from our fathers, counsel we learned at our
mother's knee. We're not keeping this to ourselves,
we're passing it along to the next generation.*
Psalm 78:1-4 ~ MSG

How are you communicating the great truths about Jesus to the
next generation?

_____

_____

_____

_____

_____

_____

_____

_____

_____

_____

_____

20____

Therefore, my beloved brothers, be steadfast, immovable, always abounding in the work of the Lord, knowing that in the Lord your labor is not in vain.

1 Corinthians 15:58 ~ ESV

Are you standing firm in God? How are you giving yourself to the work of the Lord?

20_____

You're my cave to hide in, my cliff to climb. Be my safe leader, be my true mountain guide.

Psalm 31:3 ~ MSG

How is Christ your rock and your fortress?

_____

_____

_____

_____

_____

_____

_____

_____

_____

_____

_____

_____

_____

_____

_____

_____

20____

e has shown you, O mortal, what is good.
And what does the Lord require of you? To act justly
and to love mercy and to walk humbly with your God.

Micah 6:8 ~ NIV

What does it mean for you to walk humbly?

_____

_____

_____

_____

_____

_____

_____

_____

_____

_____

_____

_____

_____

_____

_____

September 20

20_____

ow then, stand still and see this great thing the Lord is about to do before your eyes!
1 Samuel 12:16 ~ NIV

Where were you when you stopped and saw the great and mighty things the Lord was doing? And what did you see?

_____

_____

_____

_____

_____

_____

_____

_____

_____

_____

_____

_____

_____

_____

_____

_____

_____

_____

_____

21 September

20_____

od said, "I am holy; you be holy."
                              1 Peter 1:16 ~ MSG

How would holiness change our devotion to God?

20_____

I instruct you in the way of wisdom
and lead you along straight paths.

Proverbs 4:11 ~ NIV

How has the Lord given you instructions of wisdom?

20_____

You prepare a table before me in the presence of my enemies. You anoint my head with oil; my cup overflows.

Psalm 23:5 ~ NIV

How has God blessed you? Are you overflowing with joy?

20_____

all to me and I will answer you, and will tell you great and hidden things that you have not known.

Jeremiah 33:3 ~ ESV

What impresses you about this promise from God?

_____

_____

_____

_____

_____

_____

_____

_____

_____

_____

_____

_____

_____

_____

_____

_____

_____

_____

_____

20_____

In the morning, Lord, You hear my voice;
in the morning I lay my request before You
and wait expectantly.

Psalm 5:3 ~ NIV

What are your requests today that you want to lay before Him?

_____

_____

_____

_____

_____

_____

_____

_____

_____

_____

_____

_____

_____

_____

_____

_____

_____

September 26

20_____

To You, O Lord, I lift up my soul.

Psalm 25:1 ~ ESV

How are you lifting your soul up to God through prayer?

27 **September**

20_____

The one who calls you is faithful, and He will do it.
1 Thessalonians 5:24 ~ NIV

What has God called you to? How have you seen His
faithfulness in your calling?

_____

_____

_____

_____

_____

_____

_____

_____

_____

_____

_____

_____

_____

_____

_____

_____

_____

_____

_____

20_____

And now these three remain: faith, hope, and love.
But the greatest of these is love.

1 Corinthians 13:13 ~ NIV

How can love be more evident in your life?

20_____

*But as for me, it is good to be near God.
I have made the Sovereign Lord my refuge;
I will tell of all your deeds.*

Psalm 73:28 ~ NIV

How is the Lord your refuge?

20_____

My sheep recognize my voice
and I know who they are.
They follow me and I give them eternal life.
                                    John 10:27-28 ~ Phillips

How do you recognize the Father's voice?

_____

_____

_____

_____

_____

_____

_____

_____

_____

_____

_____

_____

_____

_____

_____

_____

_____

Fall

October

20_____

As each has received a gift, use it to serve one another, as good stewards of God's varied grace.

Peter 4:10 ~ ESV

Who has loved you by their service? How did this touch your heart?

_____

_____

_____

_____

_____

_____

_____

_____

_____

_____

_____

_____

_____

_____

_____

_____

20_____

$\mathcal{I}$ will give you a new heart and put a new spirit in you; I will remove from you your heart of stone and give you a heart of flesh.

Ezekiel 36:26 ~ NIV

What is the evidence in your life of a new heart?

_____

_____

_____

_____

_____

_____

_____

_____

_____

_____

_____

_____

_____

_____

_____

_____

*L*isten to my words, Lord, consider my lament.
Hear my cry for help, my King and my God,
for to you I pray.

Psalm 5:1-2 ~ NIV

Do you believe your King hears and listens to your cries for
help? How have you seen those prayers answered?

_____

_____

_____

_____

_____

_____

_____

_____

_____

_____

_____

_____

_____

_____

_____

_____

_____

_____

_____

20_____

Let us not give up the habit of meeting together, as some are doing. Instead, let us encourage one another all the more, since you see that the Day of the Lord is coming nearer.

Hebrews 10:25 ~ GNT

How are you tied in with other Christians so that you can do life together?

*H*e tends His flock like a shepherd: He gathers the lambs in His arms and carries them close to His heart; He gently leads those that have young.

Isaiah 40:11 ~ NIV

How does knowing that God carries us close to His heart encourage you?

_____

_____

_____

_____

_____

_____

_____

_____

_____

_____

_____

_____

_____

_____

_____

_____

_____

ctober

20_____

*A*gain I tell you, it is easier for a camel to go through the eye of a needle than for someone who is rich to enter the Kingdom of God.

Matthew 19:24 ~ NIV

What does this verse say to you about what pleases God and what doesn't?

$\mathcal{O}$ctober

$\mathcal{T}$he Lord is with me; I will not be afraid.
What can mere mortals do to me?

Psalm 118:6 ~ NIV

How does the presence of God reassure you regarding fear?

20_____

The Spirit you received does not make you slaves, so that you live in fear again; rather, the Spirit you received brought about your adoption to sonship. And by him we cry, "Abba, Father."

Romans 8:15 ~ NIV

In your heart, what is the difference between being a slave to fear and receiving the Spirit of sonship?

$\mathcal{O}$ctober

$\mathcal{9}$

20_____

$\mathcal{F}$or the Lord your God is a merciful God.
He will not leave you or destroy you or forget the
covenant with your fathers, that He swore to them.

Deuteronomy 4:31 ~ ESV

What does this verse tell you about God's faithfulness to His
promises?

_____

_____

_____

_____

_____

_____

_____

_____

_____

_____

_____

_____

_____

_____

_____

_____

_____

_____

_____

20_____

he Sovereign Lord is my strength;
He makes my feet like the feet of a deer,
He enables me to tread on the heights.

Habakkuk 3:19 ~ NIV

How is the Lord your strength?

$\mathcal{O}$ctober

20_____

*$\mathcal{B}$ut when He, the Spirit of truth, comes,
He will guide you into all the truth. He will not speak
on His own; He will speak only what He hears,
and He will tell you what is yet to come.*

John 16:13 ~ NIV

How has the Spirit of truth guided you into truth?

20_____

earch me, O God, and know my heart;
try me, and know my anxieties;
and see if there is any wicked way in me,
and lead me in the way everlasting.

Psalm 139:23~24 ~ NKJV

Spend time writing a prayer of repentance.

20_____

*He who trusts in his own heart is a fool,
but whoever walks wisely will be delivered.*

Proverbs 28:26 ~ NKJV

What does it mean to walk wisely?

20_____

he Lord make His face shine on you
and be gracious to you.

Numbers 6:25 ~ NIV

Describe a moment you have felt His face shine on you and
He was gracious to you.

_____

_____

_____

_____

_____

_____

_____

_____

_____

_____

_____

_____

_____

_____

_____

_____

_____

_____

_____

October 15

20_____

*The Lord turn His face toward you
and give you peace.*

Numbers 6:26 ~ NIV

Do you know this peace that passes all understanding?
Describe it.

20_____

My God shall supply all your needs according to His riches in glory by Christ Jesus.

Philippians 4:19 ~ KJV

How has God supplied all of your needs? How has this given glory to God?

_____

_____

_____

_____

_____

_____

_____

_____

_____

_____

_____

_____

_____

_____

_____

_____

_____

$\mathcal{O}$ctober

20_____

$\mathcal{A}$*rise, shine; for your light has come,*
and the glory of the Lord has risen upon you.

Isaiah 60:1 ~ ESV

In what ways is the Lord calling you to arise and go forth?

20_____

his then, is how you should pray:
"Our Father in heaven, hallowed be your name."
Matthew 6:9 ~ NIV

In what area of your life do you need to put your full trust in your Father?

$\mathcal{O}$ctober

20_____

$\mathcal{T}$*he Spirit of God has made me;*
the breath of the Almighty gives me life.

Job 33:4 ~ NIV

How has God's breath given you life?

20_____

*May you ever experience more and more
of mercy, peace, and love!*

Jude 2 ~ Phillips

Since you became a follower of Christ, how have you
experienced more of His mercy, peace, and love in your life?

20_____

The angel said to those who were standing before him, "Take off his filthy clothes."
Then he said to Joshua, "See I have taken away your sin, and I will put fine garments on you."

Zechariah 3:4 ~ NIV

What does it look like for you to take off your filthy clothes and allow Christ to put a fine garment over you?

_____

_____

_____

_____

_____

_____

_____

_____

_____

_____

_____

_____

_____

_____

_____

_____

20_____

"*When my life was ebbing away,*
I remembered you, Lord,
and my prayer rose to You, to Your holy temple."

Jonah 2:7 ~ NIV

Have you ever felt like your life was slipping away? How did the Lord rescue you?

_____

_____

_____

_____

_____

_____

_____

_____

_____

_____

_____

_____

_____

_____

_____

_____

_____

_____

20_____

So then, brothers and sisters, stand firm and hold fast to the teachings we passed on to you, whether by word of mouth or by letter.

2 Thessalonians 2:15 ~ NIV

In this verse, Paul is encouraging the Thessalonians to stand firm! How are you standing firm in God's Word?

*T*he Lord is close to the brokenhearted and saves
those who are crushed in spirit.

Psalm 34:18 ~ NIV

Have you ever felt brokenhearted? Has your spirit ever been
crushed? How did the Lord save you?

_____
_____
_____
_____
_____
_____
_____
_____
_____
_____
_____
_____
_____
_____
_____
_____
_____

*O*ctober

20_____

*H*er children arise and call her blessed;
her husband also, and he praises her.

Proverbs 31:28 ~ NIV

According to this verse, what is the response toward a mother
of noble character?

_____

_____

_____

_____

_____

_____

_____

_____

_____

_____

_____

_____

_____

_____

_____

_____

_____

20_____

For this God is our God forever and ever; He will be our guide even to the end.

Psalm 48:14 ~ NIV

How does this verse encourage you?

*O*ctober

20_____

*D*on't you know that you yourselves are God's
temple and that God's spirit dwells in your midst?
1 Corinthians 3:16 ~ NIV

How does this verse help you see yourself as made in the image
of God?

_____

_____

_____

_____

_____

_____

_____

_____

_____

_____

_____

_____

_____

_____

_____

_____

28 October

20_____

*He brought me out into a spacious place;
He rescued me because He delighted in me.*

Psalm 18:19 ~ NIV

What did He rescue you from? How does this verse encourage you, knowing that He delights in you?

*O*ctober

ut encourage one another daily, as long as it is called "Today," so that none of you may be hardened by sin's deceitfulness.

Hebrews 3:13 ~ NIV

Who do you know that needs encouragement? List some ways you can encourage others.

_____

_____

_____

_____

_____

_____

_____

_____

_____

_____

_____

_____

_____

_____

_____

_____

_____

_____

_____

30 October

20_____

*He reached down from on high
and took hold of me; He drew me out of deep waters.*

Psalm 18:16 ~ NIV

Was there a time in your life that God reached down and took
hold of you and drew you out of a difficult situation?

_____

_____

_____

_____

_____

_____

_____

_____

_____

_____

_____

_____

_____

_____

_____

*O*ctober

20____

*E*ven if you live a long time, don't take a single day for granted. Take delight in each light-filled hour, remembering that there will also be many dark days and that most of what comes your way is smoke.

Ecclesiastes 11:8 ~ MSG

How can you delight in God more?

20_____

s anyone among you suffering? Let him pray.
Is anyone cheerful? Let him sing praise.

James 5:13 ~ ESV

Let him pray! Spend time praying and praising your Father who
loves you deeply.

20_____

But I am like an olive tree
flourishing in the house of God;
I trust in God's unfailing love forever and ever.

Psalm 52:8 ~ NIV

What kind of tree represents your spiritual life? Are you
flourishing and trusting in God?

20_____

Share with the Lord's people who are in need.
Practice hospitality.

Romans 12:13 ~ NIV

How can you give lavishly to someone in need today?

November 4

20_____

$\mathcal{I}$ say to myself,
"The Lord is my portion; therefore I will wait for Him."
Lamentations 3:24 ~ NIV

How is the Lord your portion?

20____

As He spoke, He showed them the wounds
in His hands and in His side.
They were filled with joy when they saw the Lord!
John 20:20 ~ NLT

Describe a time when you exposed your wounds to someone else.

20_____

acob's well was there, and Jesus, tired as He was from the journey, sat down by the well.
It was about noon.

John 4:6 ~ NIV

How is Jesus causing you to stop and rest in your journey?

_____
_____
_____
_____
_____
_____
_____
_____
_____
_____
_____
_____
_____
_____
_____
_____
_____

20_____

Don't burn out; keep yourselves fueled and aflame.
Be alert servants of the Master.

Romans 12:11 ~ MSG

How has God called you to be a servant? How is He wanting
you to pace yourself?

_____

_____

_____

_____

_____

_____

_____

_____

_____

_____

_____

_____

_____

_____

_____

_____

20_____

My heart says to you, "Seek His face!"
Your face, Lord, I will seek.

Psalm 27:8 ~ NIV

Make a list of ways you seek Him.

20____

Think about the things of heaven,
not the things of earth.

Colossians 3:2 NLT

If you set your thoughts on Christ and heaven, how would your life change?

_____

_____

_____

_____

_____

_____

_____

_____

_____

_____

_____

_____

_____

_____

_____

_____

_____

November 10

20_____

*"**I** do know that Messiah is coming.
When He arrives , we'll get the whole story."
"I am He," said Jesus. "You don't have to wait any
longer or look any further."*
John 4:25-26 MSG

How has the Messiah awaken in you a yearning for intimacy?

20_____

In fact, everyone who wants to live a godly life in Christ Jesus will be persecuted.

2 Timothy 3:12 ~ NIV

Have you ever experienced persecution? How did the situation call you to stand firm in Christ?

_____

_____

_____

_____

_____

_____

_____

_____

_____

_____

_____

_____

_____

_____

_____

_____

_____

November 12

20_____

O my Strength, I will sing praises to you,
for you, O God, are my fortress,
the God who shows me steadfast love.

Psalm 59:17 ~ ESV

How has God been your fortress and a refuge in times of
distress?

_____

_____

_____

_____

_____

_____

_____

_____

_____

_____

_____

_____

_____

_____

_____

_____

_____

_____

_____

20_____

wife of noble character who can find?
She is worth more than rubies.

Proverbs 31:10 ~ NIV

Why is character more important than deeds?

November 14

20_____

Be hospitable to each other without secretly
wishing you hadn't got to be!

1 Peter 4:9 ~ Phillips

How do you practice hospitality with joy?

20____

That Sunday evening the disciples were meeting behind doors because they were afraid of the Jewish leaders. Suddenly, Jesus was standing there among them ! "Peace be with you." He said.

John 20:19 ~ NLT

Describe how your soul responds to hearing Jesus grant you peace from fear.

_____

_____

_____

_____

_____

_____

_____

_____

_____

_____

_____

_____

_____

_____

_____

_____

20_____

Commit your way to the Lord, trust also in Him,
and He shall bring it to pass.

Psalm 37: 5 ~ NKJV

What do you worry about the most? Can you trust in Jesus to
bring it to pass?

20____

Where no counsel is, the people fall:
but in the multitude of counsellors there is safety.
Proverbs 11:14 ~ KJV

Can you take advice? Do you allow others to give you counsel?
Explain your thoughts.

_____

_____

_____

_____

_____

_____

_____

_____

_____

_____

_____

_____

_____

_____

_____

_____

_____

November 18

20_____

*or God has not given us a spirit of fear,
but of power and of love and of a sound mind.*
2 Timothy 1:7 ~ NKJV

Define these words: fear, power, love, and a sound mind!

20_____

*or great is His love toward us, and the
faithfulness of the Lord endures forever.*

Psalm 117:2 ~ NIV

How is God's love and faithfulness different than what the
world offers?

esus replied, "Very truly I tell you, no one can see the kingdom of God unless they are born again."

John 3:3 ~ NIV

What do think it means to be born again? Have you experienced this personally?

_____

_____

_____

_____

_____

_____

_____

_____

_____

_____

_____

_____

_____

_____

_____

_____

21 November

20_____

See, I am doing a new thing! I am making a way in the wilderness and streams in the wasteland.

Isaiah 43:19 ~ NIV

What new things is God doing in your wilderness?

_____

_____

_____

_____

_____

_____

_____

_____

_____

_____

_____

_____

_____

_____

_____

_____

_____

_____

November 22

20_____

o you nothing out of selfish ambition or vain conceit. Rather, in humility value others above yourselves, not looking to your own interests but each of you to the interests of the other.

Philippians 2:3-4 ~ NIV

What is one step you can take to grow in humility?

20_____

Surely your goodness and love will follow me all the days of my Life, and I will dwell in the house of the Lord forever.

Psalm 23:6 ~ NIV

How does this verse give you hope?

_____

_____

_____

_____

_____

_____

_____

_____

_____

_____

_____

_____

_____

_____

_____

_____

_____

_____

 ovember 24

20____

Always give thanks to God the Father for everything, in the name of our Lord Jesus Christ.
Ephesians 5:20 ~ NIV

Take time to write a note to God for a blessing and for a problem.

20_____

The Lord is my strength and my shield;
my heart trusts in Him, and I am helped.

Psalm 28:7 ~ HCSB

How has the Lord been your strength and shield? How has that
encouraged you to trust in Him?

November 26

20_____

Your father knows what you need
before you ask Him.

Matthew 6:8 ~ NIV

Describe a moment when your Father knew your need before
you asked Him.

27 November

20_____

Create in me a pure heart, O God,
and renew a steadfast spirit within me.

Psalm 51:10 ~ NIV

What needs to be purged from your life to create in you a pure and steadfast heart?

20_____

eace I leave with you; My peace I give you.
John 14:27 ~ NIV

How has your Savior given you peace?

20_____

*"Forget the former things
and do not dwell on the past."*

Isaiah 43:18 NIV

How do you press forward?

 November 30

20_____

She is a tree of life to those who take hold of her;
those who hold her fast will be blessed.

Proverbs 3:18 ~ NIV

In this proverb, what is the author using "tree of life" to
describe?

20_____

*He determines the numbers of the stars
and calls them by name.*

Psalm 147:4 ~ NIV

How do you believe that He can keep track of all the details of your life?

_____

_____

_____

_____

_____

_____

_____

_____

_____

_____

_____

_____

_____

_____

_____

_____

_____

20_____

*Your path led through the sea,
your way through the mighty waters,
though your footprints were not seen.*

Psalm 77:19 ~ NIV

What circumstances are you facing that feel like a vast ocean in front of you? How is God asking you to trust Him through the waves?

20_____

"*I've loved you the way my Father has loved me.
Make yourself at home in my love.*"

John 15:9 ~ MSG

Let's imagine what this would look like for you to make yourself at home in Fathers love! What would it look like for you personally?

_____

_____

_____

_____

_____

_____

_____

_____

_____

_____

_____

_____

_____

_____

_____

_____

_____

_____

December 4

20____

$how proper respect to everyone: Love the brotherhood of believers, fear God, honor the King.

1 Peter 2:17 ~ NIV

How can you show respect to everyone, love other believers, and fear God?

20_____

onor your father and mother.
Matthew 19:19 ~ NIV

Describe a time in your life when you honored your parents by supporting them.

December 6

20____

*Lord, our Lord, how majestic is your name
in all the earth!*

Psalm 8:9 ~ NIV

What does majestic mean? How is God Majestic to you?

20_____

herefore my heart is glad, and my glory rejoiceth: my flesh also shall rest in hope.

Psalm 16:9 ~ KJV

What makes your heart glad?

_____

_____

_____

_____

_____

_____

_____

_____

_____

_____

_____

_____

_____

_____

_____

_____

_____

_____

20_____

"*Holy, Holy, Holy*
is the Lord God Almighty,
who was, and is, and is to come."

Revelation 4:8 ~ NIV

How have you experienced God's Holiness?

20_____

Keep yourselves in God's love as you wait
for the mercy of our Lord Jesus Christ
to bring you to eternal life.

Jude 1:22 ~ NIV

How do you keep yourself in God's love?

_____

_____

_____

_____

_____

_____

_____

_____

_____

_____

_____

_____

_____

_____

_____

_____

_____

20_____

*So Christ was sacrificed once to take away the sins
of many; and He will appear a second time,
not to bear sin, but to bring salvation
to those who are waiting for him.*

Hebrews 9:28 ~ NIV

Is your heart and soul ready for Him? Explain your answer.

20_____

Is anyone of you in trouble? Let them pray.
Is anyone happy? Let them sing songs of praise.

James 5:13 ~ NIV

Spend a few moments giving praise and requesting your needs before God!

 December

20_____

We must pay the most careful attention, therefore, to what we have heard, so that we do not drift away.
Hebrews 2:1 ~ NIV

How is this Hebrews scripture warning us to pay attention?

_____

_____

_____

_____

_____

_____

_____

_____

_____

_____

_____

_____

_____

_____

_____

_____

_____

20_____

*Therefore, since the promise of entering His rest
still stands, let us be careful that none of you
be found to have fallen short of it.*

Hebrews 4 :1 ~ NIV

How are you entering into His rest by faith?

20____

And my God will meet all your needs according to the riches of his glory in Christ Jesus.

Philippians 4:19 ~ NIV

What are some of your needs that you need to place before God?

20_____

"Our God, will you not judge them? For we have no power to face this vast army that is attacking us. We do not know what to do, but our eyes are on you."

2 Chronicles 20:12 ~ NIV

Describe a time in your life when God delivered you from a situation that seemed impossible.

20_____

ere's what I want you to do: Find a quiet, secluded place so you won't be tempted to role-play before God. Just be there as simply and honestly as you can manage. The focus will shift from you to God, and you will begin to sense his grace.

Matthew 6:6 ~ MSG

Where is your private room?

_____

_____

_____

_____

_____

_____

_____

_____

_____

_____

_____

_____

_____

_____

20____

"*For where your treasure is,
there your heart will be also.*"

Matthew 6:21 ~ NIV

What does this verse tell you about the importance of what is in
your heart?

_____
_____
_____
_____
_____
_____
_____
_____
_____
_____
_____
_____
_____
_____
_____
_____

20_____

*"Therefore do not worry about tomorrow,
for tomorrow will worry about itself.
Each day has enough trouble of its own."*

Matthew 6:34 ~ NIV

What worries are you troubled with that you need to release?

_____

_____

_____

_____

_____

_____

_____

_____

_____

_____

_____

_____

_____

_____

_____

20_____

$\mathcal{B}$ut the angel said to her,
"Do not be afraid, Mary; you have found favor with
God. You will conceive and give birth to a son,
and you are to call him Jesus."

Luke 1:30-31 ~ NIV

Imagine this moment, and make a list of emotions Mary must have felt.

December 20

20_____

When Joseph woke up,
he did what the angel of the Lord had commanded him
and took Mary home as his wife.

Matthew 1:24 ~ NIV

For Mary and Joseph, Christmas began with submitting
themselves to God. Describe a moment when you submitted
yourself to God. What were your challenges and blessings?

_____

_____

_____

_____

_____

_____

_____

_____

_____

_____

_____

_____

_____

_____

_____

_____

_____

20_____

"I am the Lord's servant,"
Mary answered. "May your word to me be fulfilled."
Then the angel left her.

Luke 1:38 ~ NIV

How are you the Lord's servant?

20_____

*The Word became flesh and made His dwelling
among us. We have seen His glory,
the glory of the one and only Son,
who came from the Father, full of grace and truth.*

John 1:14 ~ NIV

How have you seen His glory?

_____

_____

_____

_____

_____

_____

_____

_____

_____

_____

_____

_____

_____

_____

_____

_____

_____

20_____

For the Son of Man came to seek and to save that which was lost.

Luke 19:10 ~ ASV

Spend time thanking God for this wonderful and glorious hope.

20_____

And she brought forth her firstborn son,
and wrapped Him in swaddling clothes,
and laid Him in a manger;
because there was no room for them in the inn.

Luke 2:7 ~ KJV

Is there room for Christ in your busy life? Is there room in your heart for Him?

20_____

oday in the town of David a Savior has been born to you; He is the Messiah, the Lord.

Luke 2:11 ~ NIV

Jesus Christ is here. He is here to give hope, to forgive our sins, to give us a new song, to impart faith, and to heal our spiritual wounds. Will you let Him be the Messiah in your life?

20_____

or unto us a child is born, unto us a son is given;
and the government will be upon His shoulder.
And His name will be called Wonderful, Counselor,
Mighty God, Everlasting Father, Prince of Peace.

Isaiah 9:6 ~ NKJV

Which name is most meaningful to you and why?

27 December

20_____

They entered the house and saw the child in the arms of Mary, his mother. Overcome, they kneeled and worshiped Him. Then they opened their luggage and presented gifts: gold, frankincense, myrrh.

Matthew 2:11 ~ MSG

How is God calling you to be fully devoted to Him?

20_____

"I am the Alpha and the Omega,"
says the Lord God, "who is, and who was,
and who is to come, the Almighty."

Revelation 1:8 ~ NIV

How is Jesus your "I AM"?

20_____

The Lord bless you and keep you.

Numbers 6:24 ~ NIV

How have you enjoyed the Lord being near you?

20_____

But those who hope in the Lord will renew their strength. They will soar on wings like eagles; they will run and not grow weary, they will walk and not be faint.

Isaiah 40:31 ~ NIV

How will the truths from this passage affect the way you walk this next year?

31 December

20_____

*he grace of our Lord Jesus Christ be with you all.
Amen*

Revelation 22:21 ~ NIV

Describe how God's grace has been with you during the past
365 days.

_____
_____
_____
_____
_____
_____
_____
_____
_____
_____
_____
_____
_____
_____
_____
_____
_____
_____
_____
_____

randrretreats.jimdo.com

CPSIA information can be obtained
at www.ICGtesting.com
Printed in the USA
LVOW06*0232090617

537449LV00007B/11/P

9 780997 162578